CW00958065

和 月 伸 宏

NOBUHIRO WATSUKI

'LEAN, ORGANIZE, 'RRANGE

'S BEEN A YEAR NOW SINCE WE'VE
)VED INTO THE NEW STUDIO. IT'S
)OMY, BUT ALREADY IT'S GETTING CLUT-
_RED, SO WE INITIATED A SERIOUS CLEAN-
UP...WITH RESULTS ILLUSTRATED HERE.
HALF THE BOOKS ARE RESEARCH, SO THEY
CAN'T JUST GO INTO THE CLOSET. AS FOR
THE ACTION FIGURES...WELL, THAT'S BEEN
OUT OF CONTROL SINCE I FIRST GOT MY
HANDS ON THE "SPAWN" SERIES. WHAT I
REALLY NEED? TIME, A HOUSEKEEPER, OR
A WIFE....

Rurouni Kenshin, which has found
fans not only in Japan but around
the world, first made its appearance
in 1992, as an original short story in
Weekly Shonen Jump Special. Later
rewritten and published as a regular,
continuing *Jump* series in 1994,
Rurouni Kenshin ended serialization
in 1999 but continued in popularity,
as evidenced by the 2000 publication of *Yahiko no Sakabatô*
("Yahiko's Reversed-Edge Sword")
in *Weekly Shonen Jump*. His most
current work, *Busô Renkin*
("Armored Alchemist"), began publication in June 2003, also in *Jump*.

RUROUNI KENSHIN VOL. 14
Gollancz Manga Edition

STORY AND ART BY
NOBUHIRO WATSUKI

English Adaptation/Gerard Jones
Translation/Kenichiro Yagi
Touch-Up Art & Lettering/Steve Dutro
Design/Matt Hinrichs
Editor/Avery Gotoh
UK Cover Adaptation/Sue Michniewicz

RUROUNI KENSHIN ©1994 by Nobuhiro Watsuki. All rights reserved.
First published in Japan in 1994 by SHUEISHA Inc., Tokyo. English
publication rights in United Kingdom arranged by SHUEISHA Inc. through
VIZ Media, LLC, U.S.A., Tuttle-Mori Agency, Inc., Japan, and Ed Victor Ltd., U.K.
This edition published in Great Britain in 2007 by Gollancz Manga, an imprint of
the Orion Publishing Group, Orion House, 5 Upper St Martin's Lane, London
WC2H 9EA, and a licensee of VIZ Media, LLC.

1 3 5 7 9 10 8 6 4 2

The right of Nobuhiro Watsuki to be identified as the author
of this work has been asserted by him in accordance with
the Copyright, Designs and Patents Act 1988.

A CIP catalogue record for this book is
available from the British Library

ISBN 978 0 57508 075 1

Printed and bound by GGP Media GmbH Poessneck, Germany

PARENTAL ADVISORY
Rurouni Kenshin is rated T+ for Teen Plus. Contains realistic
and graphic violence. Recommended for older teens (16 and up)

The Orion Publishing Group's policy is to use papers that are natural,
renewable and recyclable products and made from wood grown in sustainable
forests. The logging and manufacturing processes are expected to conform to
the environmental regulations of the country of orgin.

www.orionbooks.co.uk

MEIJI
SWORDSMAN
ROMANTIC
STORY

Vol.14
THE TIME
IS NOW

STORY & ART BY
NOBUHIRO
WATSUKI

緋村剣心（人斬り抜刀斎）
Himura Kenshin
(Hitokiri Battōsai)

神谷 薫
Kamiya Kaoru

相楽左之助
Sagara Sanosuke

明神弥彦
Myōjin Yahiko

巻町 操
Makimachi Misao

斎藤 一
Saitō Hajime

魚沼宇水
Uonuma Usui

四乃森蒼紫
Shinomori Aoshi

◆ C A S T ◆

Once he was *hitokiri*, an assassin, called Battōsai. His name was legend among the pro-Imperialist or "patriot" warriors who launched the Meiji Era. Now, Himura Kenshin is *rurouni*, a wanderer, and carries a reversed-edge *sakabatō* to prohibit himself from killing.

志々雄真実

Shishio Makoto

駒形由美

Komagata Yumi

T H U S F A R

Kenshin has journeyed to Kyoto to block the machinations of Shishio Makoto, the man who took his place as *hitokiri*. After him come Kaoru, Yahiko, Sanosuke...and a man who is out to kill him, Shinomori Aoshi. Along the way, Kenshin falls in with a girl who intensely admires Aoshi (Misao) and eventually fights a duel with Sōjirō, one of Shishio's *Juppongatana* or "Ten Swords." With his first *sakabatō* broken and new *sakabatō*, "Shinuchi," in hand, Kenshin seeks out Hiko Seijūrō, master of the Hiten Mitsurugi-ryū, to obtain the ultimate secret of that school: *Amakakeru Ryū no Hirameki*. Together with Sanosuke and Saitō, he heads off Shishio's plans to burn down Kyoto and attack Tokyo by cannon from a battleship, leading to a final battle at Shishio's lair...a battle to which Kenshin goes promising Misao that he'll bring back Aoshi. First, Sanosuke fights the fallen priest, "Bright King" Anji, whom he met on the road to Kyoto and who, ironically, taught him the powerful technique, "Mastery of Two Layers." Anji's dream is to reform the world in memory of children killed while under his protection—but it's a violent reform. Sanosuke's passion to protect enables him to add even more power to the blow and create a "Mastery of Three Layers," and so overcome Anji. Telling his foe that the dead children would not want yet more blood, but Anji's happiness alone, Sanosuke convinces Anji to lower the fists which, in anger, he had raised....

CONTENTS

RUROUNI KENSHIN
Meiji Swordsman Romantic Story
BOOK FOURTEEN: THE TIME IS NOW

RUROUNI KENSHIN

るろうに剣心

魚沼宇水

UONUMA USUI

伸宏和月

Act 112

Onward

ARE YOU ALL RIGHT?

IT'S YOUR OWN FAULT. YOU SHOULD HAVE LISTENED TO MY ADVICE AND ABANDONED YOUR DEFENSE.

SHF

OW OW OW!

YOU'RE NOT THINKING *YOU* COUNT...?

YOU HAVEN'T EVEN A RIGHT HAND...

THE WAY YOU KEPT HAMMERING AWAY, YOU MUST HAVE SHATTERED YOUR BONES.

NOW THERE ARE SEVEN REMAINING ASSASSINS ... ...AND ONLY *TWO* OF US.

WHAT?!

TWO ?!

9

NO WAY I COME THIS FAR AND LEAVE WITHOUT EVEN SEEING SHISHIO'S F—

YOU HAD BEST BE JOKING.

GRIP!!

YOU SHOULD GO.

THE INJURED WILL ONLY HOLD US BACK.

...YOU REALLY ARE STUPID LATELY, AREN'T YOU.

WOBBLE

THROB THROB

OW! OW! OW!

GIMME THAT.

ZIP

ANJI!

WELL, AT LEAST THE BLEEDING'S STOPPED.

KLIK

WE'LL STABILIZE YOUR HAND WITH A WRAP.

10

EVEN MEGUMI-DONO'S MEDICINE...

...CAN'T HEAL THAT WOUND.

12

PEOPLE... ARE NOT SO EASILY...

...SAVED... BY KINDNESS.

I KNOW. THAT LESSON...

...I LEARNED TEN YEARS AGO.

EVEN SO.

UP TILL THE MOMENT OF THEIR DEATH, THOSE KIDS IN THAT MEMORIAL TABLET...

...THEY THRIVED ON THAT KINDNESS.

THERE MUST BE 150 OF THEM!

WE'RE COMPLETELY SURROUNDED!

WE'RE HERE. THE SECOND HALL.

HYOO

SPARE US THE BUILD-UP.

ONCE YOU OPEN THE DOORS, YOU CAN'T GO B—

YOU WON'T GET AWAY WITH THIS...!

IF USUI WINS, YOU TWO ARE NEXT!!

DM DM DM D-M

ARE WE AT THE NEXT HALL YET?!

I'LL HOLD YOU TO THAT.

...

Saitō's Shingan

Results of the 2nd Popularity Poll!

9th Place:
Hiko Seijūrō
2,446 Votes

5th Place:
Saitō Hajime
3,418 Votes

6th Place:
Seta Sōjirō
3,224 Votes

4th Place:
Kamiya Kaoru
3,488 Votes

1st Place:
Himura Kenshin
21,292 Votes

Act 113
Usui's Shingan,

10th Place:
Yūkyūzan Anji
1,814 Votes

3rd Place:
Shinomori Aoshi
4,871 Votes

2nd Place:
Sagara Sanosuke
10,433 Votes

8th Place:
Makimachi Misao
2,759 Votes

7th Place:
Myōjin Yahiko
3,181 Votes

11th: Sagara Sōzō 12th: Shishio Makoto 13th: Okita Sōshi
14th: Takani Megumi 15th: Sanjō Tsubame 16th: Kamatari
17th: Uonuma Usui 18th: Arai Iori/Udō Jin-e (and so on...)

YOUR "MIND'S EYE" IS NO WITCHCRAFT.

MM. JUST AS I THOUGHT.

SHR

YOU MAY BE ABLE TO READ THE *HEART*, BUT NOT THE *THOUGHTS*.

ONCE WE'VE TAKEN ON THAT DUTY, WE ACCEPT THAT DEATH MUST BE PART OF IT. TO OBSESS OVER *EVERY* LIFE, AS DOES BATTŌSAI, IS FOLLY.

THE POLICE ARE LIKE THE SHINSENGUMI— OUR DUTY IS TO DEFEND JAPAN'S LAWS, AND THE LIVES OF ITS PEOPLE.

BUT REVENGE? I HOLD NOT ONE THOUGHT OF IT.

IT IS MY DUTY TO FINISH THIS MATTER SO THAT THOSE WHO DIED MAY PASS SAFELY INTO THE AFTERLIFE.

WHAT DRIVES ME SO "DEEP"...?

SS

IF YOUR "SHINGAN" WON'T TELL YOU, *I* WILL...

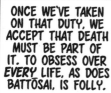

HO. ONLY
THREE
WOUNDS.
NOT
BAD.

HEH

HOW DID THIS BLIND MAN BLOCK THE POINT OF GATOTSU?

NOT "BLIND LUCK," SURELY!

...YOU SEEM PUZZLED, CAPTAIN.

OH, YOU DO, YOU DO!

THEN I'LL TELL YOU.

HEH HEH

WELL? DO-O-O YOU...?

DO YOU WANT TO KNOW?

WHAT IT IS, IS THIS...

YOU'RE RIGHT, MY "SHINGAN" IS NO WITCH-CRAFT.

THAT DAY DURING THE BAKUMATSU, I LOST MY SIGHT TO SHISHIO.

NOW USELESS TO THE SHŌGUN, I WAS ABANDONED AND BEGAN MY DAYS IN HELL.

SO I RAN...

I WAS ABLE TO WITHSTAND THE HUNGER, BUT NOT THE THIRST.

WITH NO IDEA WHERE I WAS GOING—STUMBLING ALONG THE BORDER BETWEEN LIFE AND DEATH—I EVENTUALLY FOUND MYSELF IN THE MOUNTAINS.

I RAN, AND RAN, AND RAN...

...TOWARD THE SOUND OF WATER.

GLINT

! CRUMBLE

BKOOOM

TP

THANKS SO MUCH FOR THE "SHINGAN" EXPLANATION.

IN GRATITUDE, LET ME SHOW YOU A BIT OF *MY MIND'S EYE.*

JUST THE *HEIGHTENED AWARENESS* OF MEN WHO'VE SURVIVED ONE TOO MANY LIFE-OR-DEATH SITUATIONS. CALL IT, "INTUITIVE VISION."

HEH

...NO, NO. I HAVEN'T ANY SPECIAL HEARING.

DO TELL. THEN WHAT DOES YOUR "SHINGAN" SEE...?

HO.

WHAT'RE YOU LAUGHING AT?!

SHING

YOUR OWN "SHINGAN" IS IMPRESSIVE...

WNG

SAITŌ HAJIME...

Act 114—Fangs That Bite

Act 114

Fangs That Bite

HERE
I
COME!!

HMPH.

THE GATOTSU YOU DEPEND ON IS THE "FINISHED" VERSION OF THE *THRUST.*

THE WAY OF SHINSENGUMI IS TO POLISH ONE'S BEST MOVE TO THE REALM OF PERFECTION.

AND YET!

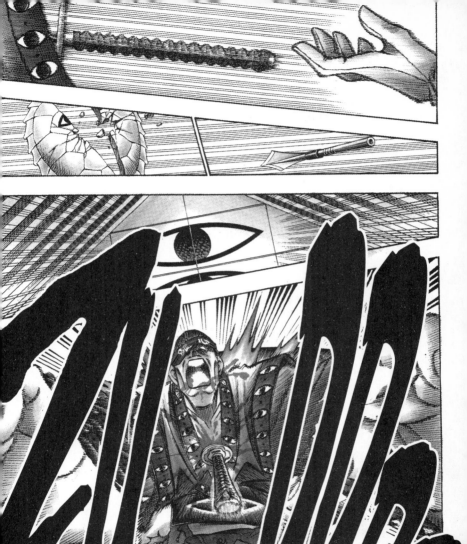

IT WAS... SUPPOSED TO...BE TO... SHISHIO.

I WASN'T SUPPOSED TO...DIE, TO YOU...

...

FEH.

I'D BEEN SAVING IT FOR MY BATTLE AGAINST BATTOSAI.

BE HONORED.

WHEN YOU LOST TO SHISHIO WITHOUT A FIGHT, YOU SHOULD HAVE ABANDONED YOUR SWORD.

YOUR MISTAKE WAS TRYING TO CHANGE THE TRUTH BY PUTTING ON AN ACT.

HOW PITIFUL.

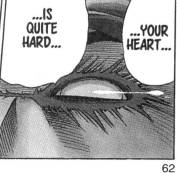

BESIDES, QUIT WHINING—WE'RE ALMOST THERE! NEXT IS THE STRONGEST OF THE JUPPONGATANA—SETA! THAT'S ONE BOY WHO WON'T BE SO EASY!

WHO ARE YOU CALLING HEAVY?!

GRR

BLAST IT, WHERE'S THE NEXT HALL?! THIS WOMAN'S HEAVY!!

SETA SŌJIRŌ...

...HE'S HERE!!

! TTRR

THAT'S HŌJI'S ROOM...AND IT'S EMPTY!

DON'T BE SO HASTY.

THAT'S NOT IT.

LET'S KEEP GOING, KENSHIN!

KENSHIN! HEY!!

The Secret Life of Characters (35)
—Uonuma Usui—

Origin-wise, he grew out of a chat with the assistants. (Several of the Juppongatana, actually, came from an assistant saying, "How about this?" Then Watsuki would go and work out the idea.) In the case of Usui, one assistant had been pushing hard for a "blind swordsman." I wasn't too thrilled with the idea originally, but then when we started talking about "Shingan"—the ability to read people's emotions by listening to their heart-beat and pulse—I decided to go with the flow.

Usui was at first supposed to fight Kenshin right after Chō—chasing him down in the city like the Terminator—but the plot started going in a different direction, and Usui ended up fighting (and dying) against Saitō. To be honest, he's a character (like Raijūta) that I regret having created. Usui is more popular than Raijūta was, though, so I'm guessing that must also mean he's stronger. (The Terminator-like Usui that I didn't end up drawing is slated to appear after the Kyoto Arc, so be watching for him.)

Though many people seem to think the model in terms of design is "Lau" from "*Virtua Fighter*," it's actually "Tao Pai Pai" from Toriyama-sensei's "*Dragon Ball*." (As the first villain in that story to defeat Gokū, he made a strong impression!) As for the eyeball-covered costume, I had envisioned a plain, tribal outfit, but when I saw the spider-like angel from "*Evangelion*," out that first idea went. (Up till about Episode 20, I was all but obsessed with "Eva"; more about that in this space as time goes on.) Since we're already on the subject, Usui was also supposed to have been a handsome, long-haired type, but when I did the rough sketch, he looked so much like "Ukyō" from "*SamuSupi*" that I thought, "Uh-oh, busted again—better not." That's when I went back to the drawing board, and the current Usui was born. Although his overall look was pulled together from several different sources, I think it came out pretty well. If I could have created a character this successful from scratch, well, I'd have no complaints, but....

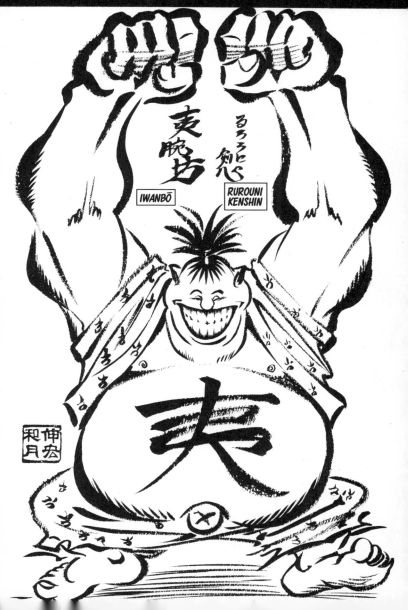

I ALREADY *TOLD* YOU!!

IS THIS ANOTHER TRICK?!

GRIP

BESIDES, HŌJI'S IN NO SHAPE TO FIGHT. HE *COULDN'T* BE HERE!

ANY "TRICKS" SO FAR HAVE BEEN *HŌJI'S* IDEA! SHISHIO-SAMA DOESN'T *DO* THAT IN A DUEL.

...THOUGH STILL A SHISHIO ALLY.

THEN WHOEVER *IS* THERE, *ISN'T* IN THE JUPPON-GATANA...

NOT *ONE* MEMBER OF THE JUPPONGATANA IS IN THAT ROOM.

IT ISN'T ...?

...IT IS.

69

...IS THE OKASHIRA OF THE ONIWABANSHŪ ONMITSU— SHINOMORI AOSHI!!

THE ONLY ONE IT CAN BE...

SO, KENSHIN... WHAT NEXT?

...

COME OUT, COME OUT, WHEREVER YOU ARE...!

THE JUPPON-GATANA HAVE COME TO PLAY!!

WHILE WE STAND HERE TALKING, AOI-YA'S IN DANGER!

WE JUST DON'T HAVE THE TIME TO WASTE...!

...AND WRAP THEM UP FOR SHISHIO-SAMA!

WE'LL CHOP OFF YOUR HEADS...

WHAT SHALL WE DO?

WHO'D'VE THUNK IT?

...THAT'S THE JUPPON-GATANA?!

HMM...

OF COURSE, IT'S NOT AS THOUGH THEY'RE JUST *ANY* THREE...

LET'S TAKE 'EM UP ON IT!

7-ON-3 BEATS 7-ON-150.

AS KAORU SAYS, THINK *DEFENSE*, NOT OFFENSE.

...IF WE CAN JUST MANAGE TO *STALL LONG ENOUGH!*

A CROWD LIKE THAT'S *BOUND* TO ATTRACT THE POLICE...

4-ON-1 GIVES US BEST ODDS.

WE'LL ALL STRIKE AT ONE AND BRING HIM DOWN QUICKLY.

THREE ON THE BEST, TWO ON THE OTHERS?

HOW SHALL WE SPLIT UP, THEN?

NO...

75

FIRST BLOOD!

GIN!

GIN!

"KU"-SHAPED SHURIKEN!

CIRCLE SHURIKEN!

THEY
DID
IT!

AOSHI...

...SO MUCH...

...IT'S HARD TO BELIEVE YOU'RE THE SAME MAN.

YOU'VE CHANGED...

TO DEFEAT YOU...

ZK ZK

89

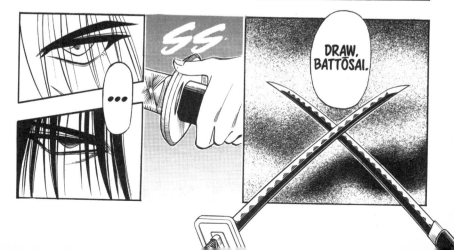

...WHAT IS THIS?

KENSHIN?!

...DO YOU MEAN TO ABANDON OUR BATTLE?

AFTER IT ALL...

ARE WE THROUGH, NOW?

IS THAT ALL...?

HE'S COMING, KENSHIN... DRAW YOUR SWORD!

HEY! DON'T TELL ME YOU WERE SERIOUS?!

TP

NO.

...AND THUS MADE TO SEE THAT THIS ONE CANNOT BE DEFEATED.

THIS NEW AOSHI WILL BE STOPPED BY THE ART OF THE TERRAIN...

— ...

...OF BRINGING BACK THE AOSHI WHO ONCE WAS.

IT MAY BE THE ONE HOPE...

THERE—!

HH

HH

NOT GOOD...

NOT GOOD AT ALL!

TK

TK

TK

"ANJI, DEFEATED... USUI, FIGHTING SAITŌ HAJIME..."

"HIMURA AND SHINOMORI AOSHI HAVE BEGUN THEIR BATTLE IN MY ROOM..."

SHISHIO-SAMA!

A TELEGRAM FROM YUMI!

ALMOST NO ONE CAN FIGHT ANJI WITHOUT BEING HURT.

NOT SO VERY BAD.

WITH THOSE OTHERS INJURED, BATTŌSAI...

PFF

AND USUI IS SURE TO GIVE SAITŌ A WOUND OR TWO, EVEN THOUGH HE'S SURE IN THE END TO LOSE.

SUCH CONFIDENCE.

...WILL BE EASILY DEALT WITH BY SŌJIRŌ AND MYSELF.

...SEE ME FLUSTERED, AND IN PANIC?

YOU'D RATHER...

PFF

...THE TIME HAS COME FOR BATTŌSAI AND AOSHI TO SETTLE THEIR SCORE.

IN ANY CASE...

HMPH

WHAT?

READY SŌ. YOUR SWORD—THOUGH YOU'VE PLENTY OF TIME.

100

THEIR BATTLE IS BOUND TO DRAG ON FOR QUITE AWHILE.

WHERE CAN HE GO, PINNED BY THAT SHELF?!

WOOSH FMP! FMP FMP FMP M

HE REALLY DID BEAT AOSHI WITHOUT DRAWING HIS—

WHEELING-SWORD "KAITEN-KENBU" DANCE

DUAL-STYLE "NITŌ-RYŪ" KODACHI

SIX SUCCESSIVE "ROKUREN" STRIKES

Act 117—Aoshi Attacks

KENSHIN!

RYŪKANSEN (DRAGON-SPIRAL STRIKE)!

HITEN MITSURUGI-RYŪ...

飛天御剣流

龍巻閃

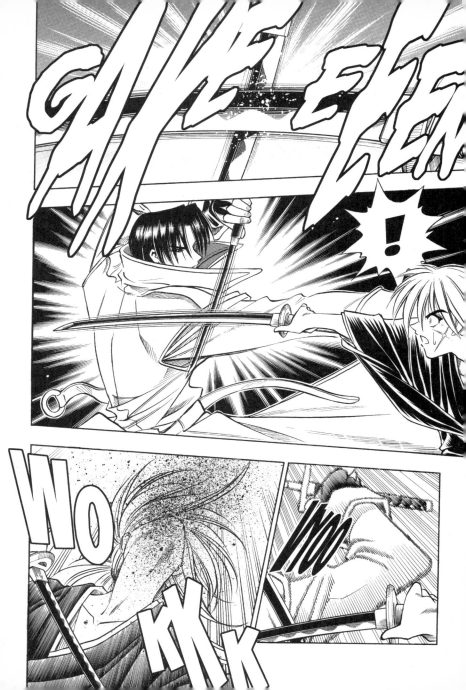

...STRONG...!

HE'S...

ZOONK

ĽHK

JUST AS YOU SAID TO ME BEFORE...

...DEFEATING YOU AS YOU ARE NOW WOULD BE NOTHING.

THE MAN I KNOW WOULDN'T FALL TO SOMETHING LIKE THIS.

GET UP, BATTŌSAI.

FOR IT IS *THAT* FOR WHICH I SACRIFICED IT ALL...

PRIDE AND COMPASSION, GOOD AND EVIL...

...WITH WHOM I TROD THE SAME PATH.

...AS WELL AS THOSE WHO TRUSTED ME...

...WHILE I HOLD IN HAND THE BLOSSOM OF GLORY.

STAND, BATTŌSAI! FOR YOU FACE YOUR DEFEAT...

AND, WITH IT, MY LIFE AS THE LAST "OKASHIRA" OF THE BAKUMATSU...

...WILL BE AT ITS END.

REVERSE YOUR SAKABATŌ, AND ANSWER MY SWORD AT FULL STRENGTH.

NOW, BATTŌSAI!

MAYBE HE DID HOLD BACK, THAT TIME WITH THE OLD MAN AT AOI-YA... BUT NOT ANYMORE.

LIVES TO FIGHT... LIVES TO DIE. HIS HUMANITY, CAST AWAY.

ALREADY HE'S GIVEN UP ON LIFE.

HE REALLY HAS THROWN IT ALL AWAY, FOR THIS.

...HE FIGHTS, EXPECTING TO DIE.

THIS MAN...

THIS IS BAD, KENSHIN. YOU CAN'T BE THINKING OF "PROMISES" NOW...!

NOW, IT'S KILL OR BE KILLED! IF YOU DON'T KILL HIM, YOU'LL DIE!

!

ZABBBBBBB

YOU COME INTO THIS BATTLE THINKING THOUGHTS LIKE THAT...?

BLUP

"END IT ALL WITH THE BLOSSOM OF GLORY IN HAND"...?

NOT *ONE* OF THEM WANTS THIS TO END IN YOUR DEATH!!

YOU'RE A FOOL!

MISAO-DONO, OKINA-DONO, HAN'NYA, SHIKIJŌ, BESHIMI, HYOTTOKO...

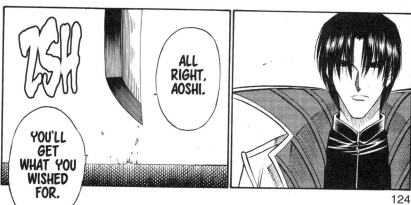

TSH

ALL RIGHT, AOSHI.

YOU'LL GET WHAT YOU WISHED FOR.

124

Act 118
Paper-Thin

THIS ONE HAS ALSO TRAINED BETWEEN LIFE AND DEATH.

SS

VP

...TO DRAW FULL POWER, WITHOUT BECOMING THE HITOKIRI BATTŌSAI.

ALSO, A WAY WAS LEARNED...

IT WAS ONLY FOR A WEEK, BUT THE SECRET OF HITEN MITSURUGI-RYŪ WAS HAD...

...AFTER RETURNING TO MASTER HIKO SEIJŪRŌ.

!

AGAIN, EMPTY WORDS.

...

COME FIGHT, AND SEE.

ARE THEY? IF SO...

IT'S OBVIOUS TALKING'S NOT GONNA DO IT FOR YOU.

WE GOT HEADS TO CRACK, AND NO TIME TO CRACK 'EM IN.

GO ON, SHINOMORI-SAN...YOU *KNOW* YOU WANT TO.

WE LET THE FIGHTING DO THE TALKING.

HOW *DO* GUYS LIKE US KNOW WHO'S WEAK, AND WHO'S STRONG...?

TECHNICALLY, YOU'RE IN NO POSITION TO DEMAND ANYTHING.

IF THE CHALLENGER ABANDONS THE FIGHT, THE WIN GOES TO KENSHIN BY DEFAULT.

BESIDES, IN THIS BATTLE, YOU'RE THE CHAL-LENGER.

BY THE WAY, KENSHIN...

WHY IS IT I HAVE YET TO HEAR ABOUT THIS "SECRET"?

SORRY.

SO MUCH ELSE TO REMEMBER...

AH, WELL. I FEEL BAD FOR YAHIKO AND THE GIRL...

TMP

...BUT AT LEAST I'LL SEE THE POWERED-UP, NON-BATTŌSAI KENSHIN FIRST.

BATTŌSAI.

YOU WILL.

IT'S
TIME.

飛天御剣流―

HITEN MITSURUGI-RYŪ...

NGH!

龍槌閃!!!

RYŪTSUISEN (DRAGON-HAMMER STRIKE)!!!

HH

HH

HH

DO YOU STILL THINK THEM "EMPTY WORDS"?

ONE WIDTH OF PAPER CLOSER, AND I'D HAVE SLICED YOUR JUGULAR.

...IT'S STILL TOO EARLY TO GLOAT.

HH

HH

...IS THE GULF BETWEEN US.

BUT THE *WIDTH* OF THAT PAPER...

BUT *ANYONE* CAN THROW AWAY THINGS THAT AREN'T WANTED— NOTHING TO IT.

AOSHI.

YOU SAY YOU'VE THROWN EVERYTHING AWAY.

BUT WHEN IT COMES TO "HEART," YOU BARELY CAST A SHADOW.

YOUR SWORDS HAVE BECOME STRONGEST OF ALL.

THIS NEED OF YOURS, AS OKASHIRA, TO OFFER THEM GLORY... THIS ONE GETS THAT.

HAN'NYA, SHIKIJŌ, BESHIMI, HYOTTOKO.

YOUR FOUR MOST TRUSTED MEN, DEAD.

WHAT ARE YOU ...?

144

Act 119—Time to Wake Up

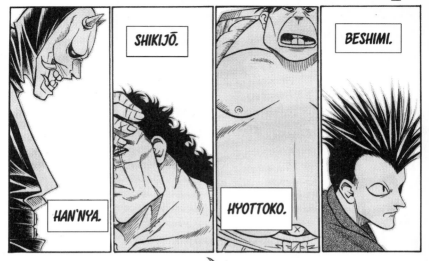

HAN'NYA.

SHIKIJŌ.

HYOTTOKO.

BESHIMI.

OR IS IT THAT THEY JUST MAKE IT EASIER?!

THE TRUTH NOW, AOSHI! IS IT FOR THEM THAT YOU FIGHT...

Act 119

Time to Wake Up

...YOU.

...SCOLD HIM WITH TRUTH THAT DIGS OUT HIS *HEART* FROM THE INSIDE...!

THE PAIN OF HAVING A MAN STRONGER THAN HIM..

...IT'S WORKING.

...TO A MAN HE SEES NOT AS AN *ENEMY*, BUT AS A PEER.

BUT IT PAINS *HIM*, TOO, HAVING TO *SAY* THAT TRUTH...

AFTER YOUR BATTLE WITH OKINA, IN ORDER TO PROTECT KYOTO AND THE ONI-WABANSHŪ...

...SHE TOOK ON THE BURDEN OF LEADERSHIP, IN YOUR STEAD.

...THAT MISAO-DONO HAS DECLARED HERSELF *OKASHIRA* OF THE ONI-WABANSHŪ?

AOSHI, DID YOU KNOW...

I'M NOT HAPPY SHE'S INVOLVED WITH THE ONIWABANSHŪ, BUT I KNOW SHE'LL DO WELL.

MISAO IS...

...A STRONG GIRL.

THEN DID YOU KNOW...

...THAT THIS "STRONG GIRL" SHED *TEARS* WHEN YOU WERE PROMISED TO BE BROUGHT BACK?

...AOSHI...

WATCH IT, KENSHIN...

HIS EYES, THEY'RE DIFFERENT.

...THE EYES FROM LONG BEFORE KANRYŪ MANSION.

YES, THEY'RE *HIS* EYES...

THAT IS SHINOMORI AOSHI!!

THAT'S THE MAN THE FOUR FOLLOWED, OKINA-DONO RESPECTED, AND MISAO-DONO ADMIRED.

WIN OR LOSE, I'VE NO REGRETS.

NO. IT'S OUR FINAL MATCH.

LEAVE NOTHING...

...AND BRING EVERY-THING!!

"FREE TALK"

Long time no see. Watsuki here. For this time's usual nonsense, let's cut straight to the games, huh? "*TenSamu*," another of the "*SamuSupi*" games, has me totally hooked. I'm in love with "*Rasetsu*"-mode Kazuki! When I first saw the character, I was thinking, "*Another* ninja?! What is this, '*Shinobi Spirits*'...?!" But then I actually played it, and oh! was it fun. Those of you who've played the game probably know, but this Kazuki hasn't got much in the way of standard moves, and with his special techniques kind of risky to use, he's best reserved for more advanced players...meaning, of course, that Watsuki can't use him to his full potential, but still he loves the character anyway. Naturally, I use Genjūrō as much as always, even with his mid-slash so slow to release, and his vulnerability during "Cherry Blossom Slash" so increased, making for a much harder time for Watsuki in general. Aside from these two, I've also taken on Nakoruru, Rimururu, Tamu-Tamu, and Ukyō, all of whom should keep me entertained until No. 5 in the series comes out. I like the looks of No. 5 already; from the flow of things, a "*ShinSamu*" follow-up would seem logical, meaning that Nakoruru will probably be brought back...and if that should happen, this time I'll be wanting the ending to be happy. (Please, SNK-*sama*!)

Another game that's got me hooked is "*Den'nō Senki Virtual On*." If you're from the "*Gundam*" era, this game should prove irresistible. Watsuki is partial to piloting the "*Temujin*," but is so feeble that its beam saber (I'm more a "slashing" kind of guy) doesn't see much action. Even so, I can now get to the last boss, Ziggurat, but...how the #@?& do I beat him?! Somebody tell me, *puriisu*...!!

...Well. For the usual nonsense, that was even more nonsensical than usual. Serious only from here on in; promise. The Kyoto Arc of "*Rurouni Kenshin*" is coming to an end [in the original Japanese serialization]. Designed to carefully balance both drama and fight scenes from the start, for the Kyoto Arc, "*RuroKen*" has been deliberately skewed toward battle. As a result, young male readers have been happy, and young female readers disappointed...which was pretty much expected. One particularly critical reader really got on my case. (At the time, I laughed—if only to get through the moment—but, later, I found myself depressed.) Why did it happen...? The reasons are more than a few, and I can't cover them all, so I won't even try. One, though, is to challenge myself as a writer: Just how much potential can I draw from fight scenes...? (Which, to be brutally frank, are the lifeblood of "*Jump*.") I enjoy deconstructing the battles of other artists, but how many had I done myself...? I decided I should just dive in, saving the self-criticism for later. But fight-scene fans are especially critical, and I've realized that that kind of manga really is hard to do well. A good battle is so much more than "just" a collection of fight scenes: as a story, it can be very worthwhile. When the Kyoto Arc is finished, the idea is to rebalance the drama and the fight scenes once more. We'll be heading into some pretty grim territory, but I'll try my best to make it fun where I can, so please continue lending your support to Kenshin and the gang's latest adventures.

See you next volume!

WHETHER IT'S KENSHIN OR WHETHER IT'S AOSHI...

THIS IS IT— THE LAST MATCH!

NO DOUBT HE'LL UNLEASH HIS KAITEN-KENBU ROKUREN...

AOSHI'S DOING A REVERSE DUAL-KODACHI, NO MISTAKE THERE.

FOR KENSHIN— WHO'S ALREADY WOUNDED— ONE MOMENT OF DELAY, ONE MISREAD INSTANT—AND HE'S DEAD.

EITHER LEFT, OR RIGHT...

...LAUNCHING SIX SUPER-FAST STRIKES ONE AFTER ANOTHER, FROM EITHER LEFT OR RIGHT.

READ THIS WAY

IT'S PROBABLY BEEN TEN MINUTES...BUT IT FEELS MORE LIKE *HOURS.*

...HOW LONG WILL THIS ...?

IS THERE A CLOCK ANYWHERE?

A CLOCK...

A CL...

FIRST STRIKE !!!

ON THE SIDE *OPPOSITE* THE DRAWN-SWORD'S ORIGIN, THE STRIKE!

THE RIGHT SIDE OF THE NECK!!

...FROM THE LEFT!!

THE ATTACK STARTS...

回天
剣舞

KAITEN-KENBU...

六連
!!

...ROKUREN!!!!

...

SHISHIO-SAMA! A TELEGRAM FROM YUMI!

HIMURA HAS JUST SHOWN HIS SECRET MOVE!!

TM

HERE'S HER DESCRIPTION! "I..."

FLIP

IT SEEMS, JUST AS AOSHI'S STRIKE WAS TO LAND, HE RELEASED HIS BATTŌJUTSU!

To Be Continued in Volume 15:
The Great Man vs. The Giant

GLOSSARY of the RESTORATION

*A brief guide to select Japanese terms used in **Rurouni Kenshin**. Note that, both here and within the story itself, all names are Japanese style—i.e., last or "family" name first, with personal or "given" name following. This is both because **Kenshin** is a "period" story, as well as to decrease confusion—if we were to take the example of Kenshin's sakabatô and "reverse" the format of the historically established assassin-name "Hitokiri Battôsai," for example, it would make little sense to then call him "Battôsai Himura."*

Himura Kenshin
Kenshin's "real" name, revealed to Kaoru only at her urging

Hiten Mitsurugi-ryû
Kenshin's sword technique, used more for defense than offense. An "ancient style that pits one against many," it requires exceptional speed and agility to master.

hitokiri
An assassin. Famous swordsmen of the period were sometimes thus known to adopt "professional" names—**Kawakami Gensai**, for example, was also known as "Hitokiri Gensai."

Ishin Shishi
Loyalist or pro-Imperialist **patriots** who fought to restore the Emperor to his ancient seat of power

Juppongatana
Written with the characters for "ten" and "swords," Shishio's Juppongatana are literally that—the ten generals or "swords" he plans to use in his overthrow of Japan

kanji
Japanese system of writing, based on Chinese characters

katana
Traditional Japanese longsword (curved, single-edge, worn cutting-edge up) of the samurai. Used primarily for slashing; can be wielded either one- or two-handed.

Kawakami Gensai
Real-life, historical inspiration for the character of **Himura Kenshin**

kenjutsu
The art of fencing; sword-arts; *kendô*

kodachi
Medium-length sword, shorter than the **katana** but longer than the **wakizashi**. Its easy maneuverability also makes for higher defensive capability.

Bakumatsu
Final, chaotic days of the Tokugawa regime

-chan
Honorific. Can be used either as a diminutive (e.g., with a small child—"Little Hanako or Kentarô"), or with those who are grown, to indicate affection ("My dear...").

"daruma doll"
A good luck/protection symbol, roly-poly "Daruma" figures (Usui calls it a "doll") are traditionally given in Japan to those starting new ventures (a birthday, the beginning of a new year, a new work project). Because it starts with both eyes "blank"—the giver inks in one eye only, with the second eye to be completed by the receiver once the wished-for goal has been achieved—it often is used as a metaphor for sight...or the lack thereof.

dojo
Martial-arts training hall

-dono
Honorific. Even more respectful than **-san**; the effect in modern-day Japanese conversation would be along the lines of "Milord So-and-So." As used by Kenshin, it indicates both respect and humility.

Edo
Capital city of the **Tokugawa Bakufu**; renamed **Tokyo** ("Eastern Capital") after the Meiji Restoration

Gatotsu
A seemingly simple move or *waza*, the **Gatotsu** of Saitô Hajime is in actuality devastatingly powerful, due both to its variety and its malleability. Should the first, seemingly simple thrust fail, for example, it easily can be modified to a sideways thrust without loss of tactical advantage. There are four different "types" of Gatotsu: *Isshiki, Nishiki,* and *Sanshiki* (Variants One, Two, and Three), as well as *Gatotsu Zeroshiki*—the final or "succession" technique which doubles or even triples the power of the original thrust.

-san
Honorific. Carries the meaning of "Mr.,"
"Ms.," "Miss," etc., but used more exten-
sively in Japanese than its English equivalent (note that even an enemy may be
addressed as "*-san*").

Shingan
Written with the characters *shin-* ("mind,"
"heart," "soul") and *-gan* ("eye," "insight"),
"Shingan" may alternately be translated as
"Soul Vision," or "Mind's Eye."

Shinsengumi
Elite, notorious, government-sanctioned and
exceptionally skilled swordsman-supporters
of the military government (**Bakufu**) which
had ruled Japan for nearly 250 years, the
Shinsengumi ("newly selected corps") were
established in 1863 to suppress the **loyalists**
and to restore law and order to the blood-
soaked streets of **Kyoto**.

shôgun
Feudal military ruler of Japan

shôgunate
See **Tokugawa Bakufu**

"Swift Death to Evil!"
Although there is some debate on who orig-
inated the term (some say it was the personal slogan of Saitô Hajime; others hold it
to be a more general motto of the
Shinsengumi itself), a more liberal transla-
tion of "*Aku • Soku • Zan*" might be "Evil Unto
Evil"...where, in this case, the "evil" would
be beheading, or death.

Tokugawa Bakufu
Military feudal government which dominat-
ed Japan from 1603 to 1867

Tokyo
The renaming of "**Edo**" to "**Tokyo**" is a
marker of the start of the Meiji Restoration

wakizashi
Similar to the more familiar **katana**, but
shorter (blade between 12 and 24 inches)

-kun
Honorific. Used in the modern day among
male students, or those who grew up
together, but another usage—the one you're
more likely to find in *Rurouni Kenshin*—is
the "superior-to-inferior" form, intended as
a way to emphasize a difference in status or
rank, as well as to indicate familiarity or
affection.

"ku-shaped" shuriken
Shuriken are, of course, the famed "throw-
ing stars" known to lovers of samurai and
ninja drama everywhere. "*Ku*-shaped"
shuriken, on the other hand, are simply
shuriken shaped like the Japanese letter/
syllable "*ku*"—in other words, the
boomerang shape shown in this manga.

Kyoto
Home of the Emperor and imperial court
from A.D. 794 until shortly after the **Meiji
Restoration** in 1868

loyalists
Those who supported the return of the
Emperor to power; **Ishin Shishi**

Meiji Restoration
1853-1868; culminated in the collapse of the
Tokugawa Bakufu and the restoration of
imperial rule. So called after Emperor Meiji,
whose chosen name was written with the
characters for "culture and enlightenment."

Okashira
Literally, "the head"; i.e., leader, boss

Oniwabanshû
Elite group of *onmitsu* or "spies" of the **Edo**
period, also known as *ninja* or *shinobi*.

patriots
Another term for **Ishin Shishi**...and, when
used by Sano, not a flattering one

rurouni
Wanderer, vagabond

sakabatô
Reversed-edge sword (the dull edge on the
side the sharp should be, and vice versa);
carried by Kenshin as a symbol of his reso-
lution never to kill again

-sama
Honorific. The respectful equivalent of **-san**,
-sama is used primarily in addressing per-
sons of much higher rank than one's self...or,
in a romantic sense, in addressing those
upon whom one is crushing, wicked hard.

As the long-delayed decisive battle between Kenshin and Shinomori Aoshi concludes, those left behind at Aoi-Ya wage their own, desperate battle against the "Ten Swords" or Juppongatana of madman Shishio Makoto. The might of one "sword" in particular seems monstrous...that is, until Kenshin's former Hiten Mitsurugi master, Hiko Seijûrô, takes the field. Will one warrior's respect for another succeed where all else has failed?

GOLLANCZ MANGA

find out more at www.orionbooks.co.uk

COMPLETE OUR SURVEY AND
LET US KNOW WHAT YOU THINK!

❏ Please do NOT send me information about Gollancz Manga, or other Orion titles, products, news and events, special offers or other information.

Name: _____

Address: _____

Town: _____ County: _____ Postcode: _____

❏ Male ❏ Female   Date of Birth (dd/mm/yyyy): ___ / ___ / _____
                    (under 13? Parental consent required)

What race/ethnicity do you consider yourself? (please check one)

❏ Asian   ❏ Black   ❏ Hispanic

❏ White/Caucasian   ❏ Other: _____

Which Gollancz Manga series did you purchase?

❏ Case Closed   ❏ Dragon Ball   ❏ Dragon Ball Z   ❏ Flame of Recca
❏ Fushigi Yûgi   ❏ Fushigi Yûgi: Genbu Kaiden   ❏ Maison Ikkoku
❏ One Piece   ❏ Rurouni Kenshin ❏ Yu-Gi-Oh!   ❏ Yu-Gi-Oh! Duelist

What other Gollancz Manga series have you tried?

❏ Case Closed   ❏ Dragon Ball   ❏ Dragon Ball Z   ❏ Flame of Recca
❏ Fushigi Yûgi   ❏ Fushigi Yûgi: Genbu Kaiden   ❏ Maison Ikkoku
❏ One Piece   ❏ Rurouni Kenshin ❏ Yu-Gi-Oh!   ❏ Yu-Gi-Oh! Duelist

How many anime and/or manga titles have you purchased in the last year?
How many were Gollancz Manga titles?

Anime	Manga	GM
❏ None	❏ None	❏ None
❏ 1-4	❏ 1-4	❏ 1-4
❏ 5-10	❏ 5-10	❏ 5-10
❏ 11+	❏ 11+	❏ 11+

Reason for purchase: (check all that apply)
- ❑ Special Offer
- ❑ Favourite title
- ❑ Gift
- ❑ In store promotion If so please indicate which store: _____
- ❑ Recommendation
- ❑ Other _____

Where did you make your purchase?
- ❑ Bookshop
- ❑ Comic Shop
- ❑ Music Store
- ❑ Newsagent
- ❑ Video Game Store
- ❑ Supermarket
- ❑ Other: _____
- ❑ Online: _____

What kind of manga would you like to read?
- ❑ Adventure
- ❑ Comic Strip
- ❑ Fantasy
- ❑ Fighting
- ❑ Horror
- ❑ Mystery
- ❑ Romance
- ❑ Science Fiction
- ❑ Sports
- ❑ Other: _____

Which do you prefer?
- ❑ Sound effects in English
- ❑ Sound effects in Japanese with English captions
- ❑ Sound effects in Japanese only with a glossary at the back

Want to find out more about Manga?
Look it up at www.orionbooks.co.uk, or www.viz.com

THANK YOU!
Please send the completed form to:

Manga Survey
Orion Books
Orion House
5 Upper St Martin's Lane
London, WC2H 9EA